"Charles Schulz is the only man we know who can make a round circle, a dash, a loop and two black spots express the following: an abiding love for Beethoven, a disillusionment with all women or an eight-day crusade of hate against a paper kite.

"If Charlie Schulz jiggles the circle, spots, dash and loop one way a comic strip character named Charlie Brown will tear your heart out with man's inhumanity to man. If he wiggles them a little differently he will set you to laughing so hard your sides will ache.

"The ability to make these little ink scratches into facial expressions is, of course, the mark of the great cartoonist—and Charlie Schulz has been voted the greatest of them all by the National Cartoonists Society."

—*New York World Telegram and Sun*

YOU'RE

A WINNER,

CHARLIE BROWN!

by CHARLES M. SCHULZ

Selected Cartoons from GO FLY A KITE, CHARLIE BROWN VOL. I

A FAWCETT CREST BOOK
FAWCETT PUBLICATIONS, INC., GREENWICH, CONN.
MEMBER OF AMERICAN BOOK PUBLISHERS COUNCIL, INC.

YOU'RE A WINNER, CHARLIE BROWN

This book, prepared especially for Fawcett Publications, Inc. comprises the first half of GO FLY A KITE, CHARLIE BROWN, and is published by arrangement with Holt, Rinehart and Winston, Inc.

Library of Congress Catalogue Card Number: 60-5911

PRINTING HISTORY

First Holt, Rinehart and Winston printing, August 1960
Second Printing, January 1961
Third Printing, May 1962
Fourth Printing, August 1963
Fifth Printing, October 1964
Sixth Printing, September 1965
Seventh Printing, January 1966
Eighth Printing, May 1966

First Fawcett Crest Printing, December 1966

Published by Fawcett World Library
67 West 44th Street, New York, N.Y.
Printed in the United States of America.

HOW'S THE BIRDHOUSE COMING ALONG, CHARLIE BROWN?
WELL, I'M A LOUSY CARPENTER, I CAN'T NAIL STRAIGHT, I CAN'T SAW STRAIGHT AND I ALWAYS SPLIT THE WOOD...
I'M NERVOUS, I LACK CONFIDENCE, I'M STUPID, I HAVE POOR TASTE AND ABSOLUTELY NO SENSE OF DESIGN..
SO, ALL THINGS CONSIDERED, IT'S COMING ALONG OKAY!
SCHULZ

SO HERE I AM STARTING A NEW YEAR..
BUT AM I ANY DIFFERENT? NOPE! I'M THE SAME OL' DOG!
DAY AFTER DAY AND YEAR AFTER YEAR... NEVER A CHANGE!
SNOOPY
SOMETIMES I MARVEL AT MY CONSISTENCY!

WELL, SCHROEDER, WHAT HAPPENED TO YOU?
I WAS LISTENING TO BEETHOVEN'S THIRD SYMPHONY... IN THE SECOND MOVEMENT THERE'S A BEAUTIFUL PASSAGE...JUST BEAUTIFUL...
WHENEVER I HEAR IT, I GET COLD CHILLS...
SO I CAUGHT COLD!
SCHULZ

LOOK OUT!!
HA! NOW, YOU'VE DONE IT! NOW YOU'VE BROKEN A LAMP, AND YOU'VE GOT NO ONE TO BLAME IT ON BUT YOURSELF!
MAYBE I COULD BLAME IT ON SOCIETY!
SCHULZ

I THINK IT'S TIME TO GO HOME AND TAKE A SHOWER..
GOING TO GET ALL CLEANED UP, EH, "PIG-PEN"?
WELL, I'VE LEARNED NEVER TO EXPECT TOO MUCH FROM A SHOWER...
I HAVE TO BE SATISFIED IF IT JUST SETTLES THE DUST!
SCHULZ

GOOD GRIEF!
YOU JUST PUT A HOLE IN MY ANNUITY!
FOR ME THIS BLANKET PROVIDES ALL THE SECURITY OF A GOOD INSURANCE PROGRAM
DID YOU NOTICE THAT I CUT A LITTLE PIECE OUT OF YOUR BLANKET, LINUS? I HAD TO MAKE A QUILT FOR MY DOLL'S BED... I HOPE YOU WON'T MIND...

WHEN I GET BIG, I'M GOING TO BE A HUMBLE LITTLE COUNTRY DOCTOR
I'LL LIVE IN THE CITY SEE, AND EVERY MORNING I'LL GET UP, CLIMB INTO MY SPORTS CAR AND ZOOM INTO THE COUNTRY!
THEN I'LL START HEALING PEOPLE...I'LL HEAL EVERYBODY FOR MILES AROUND!
I'LL BE A WORLD FAMOUS HUMBLE LITTLE COUNTRY DOCTOR!
SCHULZ

WHEN I GROW UP, I'M GOING TO BE A COUNTRY DOCTOR..
HA! I CAN JUST SEE YOU LIVING IN THE COUNTRY!
I DIDN'T SAY I'D LIVE IN THE COUNTRY...
I'LL COMMUTE FROM THE CITY IN MY SPORTS CAR!
SCHULZ

I HAD TO GET A SHOT TODAY
DID YOU? GEE, I HATE TO GET SHOTS!
WHEN I'M A DOCTOR MYSELF, THOUGH, IT'LL BE DIFFERENT.
FOR THE FIRST TIME IN MY LIFE I'LL BE ON THE RIGHT SIDE OF THE OL' NEEDLE!
SCHULZ

YOU A DOCTOR! HA! THAT'S A BIG LAUGH!
YOU COULD NEVER BE A DOCTOR! YOU KNOW WHY?
BECAUSE YOU DON'T LOVE MANKIND, THAT'S WHY!
I LOVE MANKIND.... IT'S PEOPLE I CAN'T STAND!!
SCHULZ

I ADMIRE YOUR AMBITION TO BE A DOCTOR, LINUS...
OF COURSE, EIGHT YEARS IS A LONG TIME TO STUDY, BUT THEN..
EIGHT YEARS?
GOOD GRIEF!
I THINK MAYBE I'LL BE A PRO-FOOTBALL PLAYER! C'MON, PASS THAT BALL OVER HERE! HIKE! ONE, TWO, THREE! C'MON, LET'S HAVE THAT OL' BALL!!
SCHULZ

WELL, WHAT ARE YOU DOING HERE?
GO ON HOME! WE DON'T WANT YOU AROUND HERE! WHO ASKED YOU TO COME BY IN THE FIRST PLACE? NOBODY! GO ON HOME!
YOU KNOW, IT'S A STRANGE THING ABOUT CHARLIE BROWN... YOU ALMOST NEVER SEE HIM LAUGH!
SCHULZ

SOMETIMES WHEN I GET UP IN THE MORNING, I FEEL VERY PECULIAR..
I FEEL LIKE I'VE JUST **GOT** TO BITE A CAT! I FEEL LIKE IF I DON'T BITE A CAT BEFORE SUNDOWN, I'LL GO CRAZY!!
BUT THEN I JUST TAKE A DEEP BREATH AND FORGET ABOUT IT..
THAT'S WHAT IS KNOWN AS REAL **MATURITY**!

CHARLIE BROWN WHAT WOULD BE YOUR REACTION IF SOMEONE SAID YOU COULD HAVE YOUR LIFE OVER AGAIN?
YOU MEAN EXACTLY AS I'VE LIVED IT? NO CHANGES? EVERYTHING HAPPENING JUST THE WAY IT DID BEFORE?
UH HUH ... WHAT WOULD BE YOUR REACTION?
AAAUGHH!
SCHULZ

HERE SNOOPY! I'LL THROW THE BALL, AND YOU CHASE IT! OKAY? C'MON, BOY! HERE, SNOOPY!
GOOD GRIEF! IF THERE'S ANYTHING I **DON'T** FEEL LIKE DOING, IT'S CHASING A **BALL**!
IT'S HARD TO HIDE BEHIND SOMEONE WHO'S VERTICAL WHEN YOU'RE HORIZONTAL!
SCHULZ

!
CLOMP!
PTUI!
HOW DEFT CAN YOU GET?

WHAM!
IN THE OLDEN DAYS THIS WAS KNOWN AS BRINGING THE WARRIOR HOME ON HIS SHIELD!

ONCE YOU'VE GOT A KITE IN THE AIR CHARLIE BROWN, IS IT ANY TROUBLE GETTING IT DOWN AGAIN?
WHAM!
THAT'S ONE PROBLEM I'VE NEVER HAD TO WORRY ABOUT
SCHULZ

ISN'T THE SKY A BEAUTIFUL BLUE TODAY, LINUS?
LOOK THERE...DID YOU EVER SEE ANYTHING NICER?

THIS IS MY LITTLE TOY FARM..
I'LL PUT THE BARN OVER HERE, AND I'LL PUT THE HOUSE HERE...
THEN I GUESS I'LL PUT THIS LITTLE TREE RIGHT HERE..
SCHULZ

YOU STUPID KITE! I'LL STOMP YOU!
I'LL MANGLE YOU!
I'LL KICK YOU!!
IT'S FLYING!
SCHULZ

A DOG'S LIFE IS A LONELY LIFE..
CATS HATE US...HORSES STEP ON US...WILD ANIMALS DESPISE US...
SIGH
THANK GOODNESS FOR PEOPLE!
SCHULZ

I DON'T FEEL WELL..
MY HEAD HURTS, AND EVERY TIME I MOVE IT, I GET DIZZY...
I JUST DON'T FEEL WELL...
SICKEST GUN IN THE WEST!
SCHULZ

HE'S GREAT, I TELL YOU... REALLY GREAT!
REMEMBER HOW HE USED TO SWAT THE OL' HORSEHIDE LAST SUMMER?
WELL, YOU HAVEN'T SEEN ANYTHING UNTIL YOU'VE SEEN HIM KICK THAT PIGSKIN!
WHY CAN'T THEY JUST PLAY THEIR OL' GAMES, AND LEAVE THE ANIMALS OUT OF IT?
SCHULZ

I OWE YOU AN APOLOGY "PIG-PEN".. I'VE BEEN TEASING YOU A LOT LATELY..
BUT WHO AM I TO TEASE YOU? YOU MAY BE DIRTY, BUT AT LEAST YOU HAVE CHARACTER!
ME? I'M BLAH! THAT'S JUST WHAT I AM..BLAH! I'M COMPLETELY BLAH! I WAS BORN BLAH, AND I'LL DIE BLAH!
WHEN YOU'RE LOOKING AT ME, YOU'RE LOOKING AT THE ALL-TIME NUMBER-ONE CHAMPION BLAH!!
SCHULZ

ARE YOU AND LINUS STILL FIGHTING?
NO, I HAVE A PHILOSOPHY THAT PREVENTS THAT SORT OF THING
I HAVE A PROFOUND PHILOSOPHY THAT HAS STOOD THE TEST OF TIME DIFFICULT AS IT MAY BE FOR THE LAYMAN TO UNDERSTAND..
I HAVE A PHILOSOPHY THAT HAS BEEN REFINED IN THE FIRES OF HARDSHIP AND STRUGGLE...
"LIVE AND LET LIVE!"
SCHULZ

I CAN'T THINK OF THAT WORD...
THERE'S ONE CERTAIN WORD THAT DESCRIBES YOUR PERSONALITY, CHARLIE BROWN, BUT I JUST CAN'T THINK OF WHAT IT IS...
"BLAH"?
THAT'S IT!

LOOK, YOU DON'T HAVE TO TELL ME I'M BLAH!
I KNOW I'M BLAH!
WELL, THEN THERE'S STILL HOPE FOR YOU CHARLIE BROWN...
IF YOU RECOGNIZE THIS IN YOURSELF THEN THAT'S THE FIRST STEP UP FROM BLAHDOM!
"BLAHDOM"?

HOW CAN ANYONE EVER LIKE SOMEONE AS BLAH AS I AM?!
PLEASE DON'T DESPAIR, CHARLIE BROWN..
MAYBE THERE'S A GIRL SOMEWHERE IN THE WORLD WHO IS JUST AS BLAH AS YOU... MAYBE YOU'LL MARRY HER..
AND MAYBE YOU'LL RAISE A WHOLE FLOCK OF BLAH KIDS, AND THEN MAYBE THEY'LL GO OUT AND MARRY SOME OTHER BLAH KIDS, AND..
AAUGH!

SNIF
SNIF
SNIF
AH, HA! I THOUGHT I SMELLED PIZZA!
MMMMMM
SIGH I COULD EAT A TWENTY-FOUR INCH PIZZA WITHOUT BATTING A LIP!
SCHULZ

BEETHOVEN USED TO BE FOND OF TAKING LONG WALKS IN THE COUNTRY...
HE WAS ALWAYS INSPIRED BY THE BEAUTIFUL SOUNDS OF THE COUNTRYSIDE...
YOU BLOCKHEAD, COME BACK HERE WITH THAT BALL!!
BEETHOVEN HAD IT NICE!

THESE ROCKS ARE A RELEASE FOR MY PENT-UP EMOTIONS.
WHEN I FEEL ALL TIED UP INSIDE, I JUST STAND HERE AND THROW ROCKS INTO THAT VACANT LOT!
HELLO, CHARLIE BROWN YOU BLOCKHEAD!
SOMETIMES I THINK I'M KIND OF A VACANT LOT MYSELF...
SCHULZ
8-17

YOU THINK THIS IS AN ORDINARY PILE OF ROCKS, DON'T YOU? WELL, IT ISN'T!
THESE ROCKS ARE MEANT TO BE THROWN IN ANGER! WHEN I GET REAL MAD, I THROW ROCKS AS HARD AS I CAN!!
IT JUST SO HAPPENS THAT TODAY I FEEL PRETTY GOOD
SCHULZ

THESE ROCKS ARE ESPECIALLY GROOMED TO BE HURLED IN ANGER!
AFTER YOU'VE THROWN ALL OF THEM, DO YOU GO OUT AND PICK THEM UP?
OH, YES...I KEEP USING THE SAME ROCKS OVER AND OVER..
IT'S NOT UNLIKE RUNNING THEM THROUGH A FILTER!
SCHULZ

THIS IS FOR ALL THE NASTY THINGS THEY SAID ABOUT GEORGE WASHINGTON!
THIS IS FOR PEOPLE WHO HATE LITTLE KIDS! AND THIS IS FOR PEOPLE WHO KICK DOGS!
THIS IS FOR HOT SUMMER NIGHTS! AND THIS IS FOR COLD WINTER MORNINGS! AND THIS IS FOR LIES AND BROKEN PROMISES!
DO YOU HAVE ANY REQUESTS?

THIS IS FOR PEOPLE WHO DON'T LIKE THE MAYOR! THIS IS FOR PEOPLE WHO DON'T LIKE THE GOVERNOR!
THIS IS FOR PEOPLE WHO DON'T LIKE BEETHOVEN!
YEAH! THIS IS FOR PEOPLE WHO DON'T LIKE BEETHOVEN!

I'VE DECIDED THAT THROWING ROCKS IS NO SOLUTION..
A PERSON JUST HAS TO LEARN TO DEVELOP SELF-CONTROL...
ONLY AN IDIOT COULD BE CONVINCED THAT THROWING ROCKS INTO A VACANT LOT WILL SOLVE HIS PROBLEMS!

DID IT EVER OCCUR TO YOU THAT "PIG-PEN" MIGHT BE CARRYING THE DIRT AND DUST OF SOME PAST CIVILIZATION?
NOTICE HOW THE DUST CLINGS TO HIM...
HE COULD HAVE ON HIM SOME OF THE SOIL OF ANCIENT BABYLON
SORT OF MAKES YOU WANT TO TREAT ME WITH MORE RESPECT, DOESN'T IT?
SCHULZ

JUST THINK OF IT.. THE DIRT AND DUST OF FAR-OFF LANDS BLOWING OVER HERE AND SETTLING ON "PIG-PEN"!
IT STAGGERS THE IMAGINATION! HE MAY BE CARRYING SOIL THAT WAS TROD UPON BY SOLOMON OR NEBUCHADNEZZAR OR GENGHIS KHAN!
!
THAT'S TRUE, ISN'T IT?
SUDDENLY I FEEL LIKE ROYALTY!
SCHULZ

POOR OL "PIG-PEN"
THEY SAY HE CARRIES ON HIM THE DIRT AND DUST OF ANCIENT CIVILIZATIONS...
HISTORY IS PASSING BEFORE MY EYES!
SCHULZ

I SEE WHERE THE PRICE OF HAIRCUTS MAY GO UP AGAIN..
MY DAD SAYS HE'S GOING TO BUY A PAIR OF CLIPPERS, AND CUT **MY** HAIR HIMSELF...
I HOPE HE CUTS YOUR EARS OFF!
I KEEP FORGETTING THAT CHARLIE BROWN'S DAD IS A BARBER!
SCHULZ

DID ANYONE EVER TELL YOU THAT YOU HAVE PRETTY EYES, SCHROEDER?
MUSICIANS GET UNNERVED WHEN YOU TELL THEM THAT THEY HAVE PRETTY EYES
SCHULZ

THEY'RE ALWAYS WRITING ABOUT EVIL STEP-MOTHERS!
EVERY STEP-MOTHER IN THESE FAIRY TALES IS DESCRIBED AS BEING EVIL!
DO YOU KNOW WHAT THIS AMOUNTS TO?
WHAT?
A BLANKET CONDEMNATION OF STEP-MOTHERS!
SCHULZ

SAY, I DO! I DO!! I DO!!!
NOPE, I GUESS I DON'T...
..IT'S JUST A LITTLE DIRT..
?
FOR ONE BRIEF, EXCITING MOMENT I THOUGHT I NEEDED A SHAVE!
SCHULZ

SNOWFLAKES FASCINATE ME... MILLIONS OF THEM FALLING GENTLY TO THE GROUND..
AND THEY SAY THAT NO TWO OF THEM ARE ALIKE!
EACH ONE COMPLETELY DIFFERENT FROM ALL THE OTHERS....
THE LAST OF THE RUGGED INDIVIDUALISTS!
SCHULZ

ALL RIGHT! SO IT'S SUPPERTIME!
I **KNOW** IT'S SUPPERTIME! I'LL BE WITH YOU AS SOON AS THIS PROGRAM IS OVER!
NOW JUST SIT STILL, AND ENJOY THE SHOW...
SIGH

CHARLIE BROWN, WE NEED YOUR ADVICE...
SAY A PERSON HAS A BAG OF CANDY, AND HALF OF THE PIECES HAVE COCONUT IN THEM. SAY THE PERSON SHE IS GOING TO SHARE THEM WITH CAN'T STAND COCONUT..
DOES HE HAVE TO ACCEPT THE COCONUT ONES ALONG WITH THE OTHERS IF HE THINKS SHE IS TRYING TO GET RID OF THEM BECAUSE SHE DOESN'T LIKE THEM EITHER?
I HAVE NEVER PRETENDED TO BE ABLE TO SOLVE MORAL ISSUES!
SCHULZ

CHARLIE BROWN, DO YOU THINK THAT SANTA CLAUS REALLY KNOWS HIS JOB?
OH, YES...AFTER ALL, HE'S BEEN AT IT FOR A LONG TIME..
THAT'S JUST WHAT HAS ME WORRIED...
PERHAPS IT'S TIME FOR A **YOUNGER** MAN TO TAKE OVER!
SCHULZ

THIS ROCKET BUSINESS IS FASCINATING
EVERY DAY THEY SEEM TO COME UP WITH SOMETHING NEW
FOR AWHILE THEY WERE SENDING UP DOGS... NOW THEY'RE SENDING UP MICE..
THAT'S A VERY HEALTHY TREND!

I'M GOING TO BE STAYING AT MY GRAMMA'S HOUSE FOR A FEW NIGHTS..
C.B.
HOW COME, CHARLIE BROWN?
BECAUSE MY MOTHER WENT TO THE HOSPITAL LAST NIGHT..
C.B.
MY DAD SAID SHE'LL BE ALL RIGHT...IN FACT, HE SAID SHE'LL BE HOME IN ABOUT FIVE DAYS..
FIVE DAYS? I WONDER... DO YOU SUPPOSE... I WONDER IF...NO, IT COULDN'T BE... STILL...

A BABY SISTER?
I'M A FATHER!
I MEAN MY DAD'S A FATHER! I'M A BROTHER! I HAVE A BABY SISTER!! I'M A BROTHER!
YOU DIDN'T ACT LIKE THAT WHEN I WAS BORN!
SCHULZ

SO CHARLIE BROWN HAD A BABY SISTER LAST NIGHT!
BOY, THERE SURE WAS A LOT OF EXCITEMENT AROUND HERE ABOUT MIDNIGHT...PEOPLE RUNNING IN ALL DIRECTIONS...
..CARS COMING AND GOING.. TELEPHONES RINGING...THINGS STILL HAVEN'T CALMED DOWN..
AND IN ALL THE EXCITEMENT, NOBODY HAS REMEMBERED TO FEED THE DOG!

SO YOU HAVE A NEW BABY SISTER, HUH, CHARLIE BROWN?
YES, AND I'M SO HAPPY...
HAPPY?
I SUPPOSE IT'S NEVER OCCURRED TO YOU THAT OVER-POPULATION IS A SERIOUS PROBLEM?!
SCHULZ

I GUESS CHARLIE BROWN'S NEW BABY SISTER CAME HOME TODAY..
I'D KIND OF LIKE TO GO IN, AND SEE HER...
STILL, MAYBE I'D BETTER NOT...
I'D JUST AS SOON WAIT FOR A FEW DAYS UNTIL HER EYES ARE OPEN!
SNOOPY
SCHULZ

HEY, C'MON!

CHARLIE BROWN HAD A BABY SISTER! HE'S HANDING OUT CHOCOLATE CIGARS!

CONGRATULATIONS, CHARLIE BROWN!
THANK YOU, 'PIG-PEN'..

NOT BAD...THIS SHOULD HAPPEN MORE OFTEN!
SCHULZ

YOU'RE ALWAYS AFTER PEOPLE TO MAKE NEW YEAR'S RESOLUTIONS!
WHY DO WE HAVE TO MAKE OUR RESOLUTIONS RIGHT ON JANUARY FIRST? WHAT'S WRONG WITH MAY SIXTEENTH OR SEPTEMBER TWENTY-THIRD?
WHY JANUARY FIRST?
IT'S NEATER!
SCHULZ

WHEN I GET BIG, I WANT TO BE A GREAT PHILANTHROPIST!
YOU HAVE TO HAVE A LOT OF MONEY TO BE A GREAT PHILANTHROPIST..
I WANT TO BE A GREAT PHILANTHROPIST WITH SOMEONE ELSE'S MONEY!
SCHULZ

ITS NO WONDER SOME PEOPLE GET FAT!
ALL THEY EVER DO IS EAT! ALL THEY EVER **THINK** ABOUT IS EATING!
SNOOPY
YOU CAN SAY THAT AGAIN!
SCHULZ

DO YOU EVER THINK MUCH ABOUT THE FUTURE, LINUS?
OH, YES...ALL THE TIME
WHAT DO YOU THINK YOU'D LIKE TO BE WHEN YOU GROW UP?
OUTRAGEOUSLY HAPPY!
SCHULZ

SO CHARLIE BROWN FINALLY GOT A BABY SISTER
GEE. WE NEVER GET ANY NEW BABIES AT **OUR** HOUSE
OURS EITHER..WE HAVEN'T HAD ANY NEW BABIES FOR A **LONG** TIME..
ALL **WE'VE** GOT IS THIS HERE **OLD** BABY!
SCHULZ

HAVE THEY DECIDED ON A NAME FOR YOUR SISTER YET, CHARLIE BROWN?
YES, HER NAME IS GOING TO BE SALLY!
SALLY?
SALLY... SALLY BROWN... GOOD OL' SALLY BROWN!
IT FIGURES!

WAS YOUR BABY SISTER BORN AT ACE HOSPITAL, CHARLIE BROWN?
NO, I DON'T THINK SO... WHY?
THAT'S TOO BAD..
IF SHE HAD BEEN BORN AT ACE HOSPITAL, SHE WOULD HAVE RECEIVED ALL NINE BEETHOVEN SYMPHONIES FREE!
SCHULZ

WELL, CHARLIE BROWN..HAVE YOU FELT ANY JEALOUSY SO FAR TOWARD YOUR NEW BABY SISTER?
OH, NO.. SHE'S A REAL DECENT SORT
YOU MEAN YOU HAVEN'T FELT EVEN THE LEAST BIT JEALOUS?
NO, NOT EVEN THE LEAST BIT..
YOU DRIVE ME CRAZY!
SCHULZ

YOU KNOW, SNOOPY..HAVING A BABY SISTER IS KIND OF NICE...
I DON'T THINK I'LL FEEL SO ALONE ANY MORE..
WELL, I HOPE HE'S RIGHT, BUT I WOULDN'T KNOW...I NEVER HAD ANY SISTERS OR BROTHERS
I WAS AN ONLY DOG!

I DON'T THINK IT'S RIGHT TO BRING NEW BABIES INTO THIS UNCERTAIN WORLD...THIS IS THE WRONG TIME!
WHAT ARE YOU GONNA DO WITH ALL THOSE BABIES WHO ARE LINED UP WAITING TO BE BORN?
YOU JUST CAN'T TELL THEM TO GO AWAY AND WAIT FOR ANOTHER THOUSAND YEARS, CAN YOU? CAN YOU?
NO, I GUESS YOU CAN'T..
THE WHOLE TROUBLE WITH YOU IS YOU NEVER THINK THESE THINGS THROUGH!
SCHULZ

SO THEY DECIDED TO NAME YOUR SISTER SALLY DID THEY?
WELL, SALLY IS A CUTE NAME, I GUESS..
IT MAKES YOU THINK OF A GIRL WHO IS SWEET AND GENTLE AND PRETTY AND MAYBE JUST A LITTLE BIT SHY...
...LIKE THE NAME LUCY!
SCHULZ

Hey, Violet!
WAIT UNTIL YOU SEE THE PAIR OF SLEEPERS I BOUGHT FOR LITTLE SALLY..
YOU CERTAINLY ARE A DEVOTED BROTHER, CHARLIE BROWN
WELL, I'M TRYING TO BE

STUPID DOG!
THE WHOLE WORLD COULD GET BLOWN UP ANY MINUTE AND ALL **YOU** THINK OF IS **DANCING**!!
I **COULD** THINK OF **EATING**, BUT IT'S TOO EARLY IN THE DAY!

THE TROUBLE WITH **YOU** IS YOU DON'T SHOW ENOUGH **RESPECT**
IF IT WEREN'T FOR HUMANS, YOU DOGS WOULDN'T EVEN **BE** HERE!
FROM NOW ON I WANT RESPECT!!

HERE, TAKE IT...DON'T BE SO SUSPICIOUS!
WHAT A DOG!
CHOMP CHOMP
HE'S GETTING SO HE DOESN'T TRUST ANYBODY
HE'D MAKE A GOOD HUMAN BEING!
SCHULZ

CHARLIE BROWN, YOUR HAVING A BABY SISTER HAS SET ME TO THINKING..
FIRST YOU SEE A YOUNG COUPLE LIVING IN THIS HOUSE ALL ALONE...
THEN ALONG COMES A BABY... THEN ANOTHER ONE...AND THEN ANOTHER ONE...PRETTY SOON THE HOUSE IS FULL OF LITTLE KIDS!
I KNOW WHAT YOU MEAN... THEY SEEM TO HAVE A WAY OF ACCUMULATING LIKE OLD MAGAZINES!
SCHULZ

..AND FIVE IS TWENTY-TWO..
NINETEEN HUNDRED AND FIFTY NINE PLUS TWENTY-TWO IS NINETEEN HUNDRED AND EIGHTY-ONE
?
WHEN I'M TWENTY-TWO AND SALLY IS SEVENTEEN, DO YOU THINK SHE'LL GO OUT WITH ME?
SCHULZ

THIS HAVING A BABY SISTER MAY DO A LOT FOR CHARLIE BROWN..
IT'S JUST LIABLE TO MAKE HIM INTO A NEW PERSON!
THAT'S A FRIGHTENING THOUGHT...
I CAN THINK OF NOTHING IN ALL THIS WORLD MORE OBNOXIOUS THAN A WELL-ADJUSTED CHARLIE BROWN!
SCHULZ

YOU THINK HAVING A BABY SISTER IS GREAT, DON'T YOU?
FROM NOW ON YOU'RE GOING TO HAVE TO **SHARE** THE AFFECTION OF YOUR MOTHER AND DAD! BUT YOU THINK YOU WON'T MIND THAT, DON'T YOU?
YOU THINK IT'LL BE FIFTY-FIFTY, DON'T YOU? WELL, IT WON'T! WITH A BABY SISTER, IT'LL BE FIFTY ONE-FORTY NINE! MAYBE EVEN **SIXTY-FORTY**!!
I'LL BET YOU DIDN'T REALIZE THAT FAMILY LIFE WAS SO MATHEMATICAL!
SCHULZ

YOURE SO SWEET, SNOOPY..I WISH I COULD GIVE YOU A BIG KISS, BUT OF COURSE, I CAN'T...
THE CURSE OF A FUZZY FACE!

LET'S START THE LETTER THIS WAY..."DEAR SANTA, WE HOPE YOU HAD A NICE SUMMER."...
WHAT DO YOU MEAN, "A NICE SUMMER"?
YOU KNOW... HIS VACATION... EVEN SANTA CLAUS HAS TO HAVE A VACATION..
I IMAGINE HE GOES OFF SOME PLACE TO REST, OR PLAY GOLF OR DO SOME SKIN DIVING... DON'T YOU THINK SO?
FOR SOME REASON I JUST CAN'T PICTURE SANTA CLAUS SKIN DIVING!
SCHULZ

YOU KNOW, IN A WAY, "DEAR SANTA CLAUS" IS RATHER STUFFY..
PERHAPS SOMETHING A LITTLE MORE INTIMATE WOULD BE BETTER...SOMETHING JUST A SHADE MORE FRIENDLY...
HOW ABOUT, "DEAR FATTY"?

YOU'RE REALLY LUCKY, CHARLIE BROWN...
ALL MY LIFE I WANTED A BABY SISTER... BUT WHAT DID I GET? I GOT **THIS** STUPID THING!
DEFINE, "STUPID THING."
SCHULZ

I'VE JUST COME TO REALIZE SOMETHING..
I NEVER KNEW IT BEFORE, BUT LUCY REALLY RESENTS MY HAVING BEEN BORN..SHE'S WANTED A SISTER LIKE YOU HAVE!
WELL, IT'S LIKE MY AUNT MARIAN ALWAYS SAYS, YOU CAN CHOOSE YOUR FRIENDS, BUT YOU CAN'T CHOOSE YOUR RELATIVES
YOUR AUNT MARIAN IS WONDERFULLY WISE!
SCHULZ

SO NOW IT COMES OUT! YOU'VE ALWAYS WANTED A SISTER, NOT A BROTHER!
I HAVE HALF A NOTION TO LEAVE HOME..
WELL, WHY DON'T YOU? AND TAKE THIS STUPID BLANKET OF YOURS WITH YOU!
ARE YOU TRYING TO GET RID OF ME?!
SCHULZ

IT'S TOO MUCH FOR ME TO TAKE.. I CAN'T STAND IT!
IT'S PRETTY DISHEARTENING TO FIND OUT THAT YOUR OWN SISTER WISHES YOU HAD NEVER BEEN BORN..
"NEVER BEEN BORN"... GOOD GRIEF! DO YOU KNOW WHAT THAT MEANS? JUST STOP TO THINK ABOUT IT...
WHY, THE THEOLOGICAL IMPLICATIONS ALONE ARE STAGGERING!

I'M RUNNING AWAY FROM HOME, VIOLET!
OH? I KNOW A GOOD JOKE ABOUT A LITTLE BOY RUNNING AWAY FROM HOME..
THIS MAN CAME ACROSS THIS LITTLE BOY STANDING BY THE CURB, SEE, AND HE ASKED HIM WHAT HE WAS DOING...
THE LITTLE BOY SAID, "I'M RUNNING AWAY FROM HOME, BUT I'M NOT ALLOWED TO CROSS THE STREET!"
THAT'S A RIOT!
SCHULZ

I'M SORRY IF I'VE UPSET YOU, LINUS..
OH, THAT'S ALL RIGHT.. *SNIF*
NO, I MEAN IT.. AFTER ALL, YOU **ARE** MY BROTHER
WE'RE PART OF THE SAME FAMILY... BROTHER AND SISTER...BLOOD RELATIVES...
NO MATTER HOW YOU LOOK AT IT, I'M **STUCK** WITH YOU!
SCHULZ

SNOOPY, DID YOU SEE LINUS GO BY HERE?
I'LL TICKLE YOU 'TIL YOU TELL ME! TICKLE TICKLE TICKLE TICKLE!
HEE HEE HEE HEE HEE HEE
HE WENT THAT WAY, HUH? GOOD! YOU'RE LUCKY YOU TOLD ME!
I'D MAKE A LOUSY SPY!

I THOUGHT HAVING A BABY SISTER WOULD CHANGE MY WHOLE LIFE, BUT IT HASN'T..
PEOPLE STILL HATE ME..NOBODY **REALLY** LIKES ME...I GET JUST AS DEPRESSED AS I ALWAYS DID..
POOR CHARLIE BROWN..
OF ALL THE CHARLIE BROWNS IN THIS WORLD, HE'S THE CHARLIE BROWNEST!
SCHULZ

DO YOU EVER WORRY ABOUT THE WORLD GETTING BLOWN UP CHARLIE BROWN?
IT ALL DEPENDS... WHAT DAY IS TODAY?
TUESDAY
WELL, ON TUESDAYS I WORRY ABOUT PERSONALITY PROBLEMS...
THURSDAY IS MY DAY FOR WORRYING ABOUT THE WORLD GETTING BLOWN UP!
SCHULZ

I'M JUST AMAZED BY THE WONDER OF IT ALL..
FIRST MY DAD BUYS A BARBER SHOP, THEN HE GETS MARRIED, THEN I'M BORN AND NOW SALLY IS BORN..
OUR FAMILY IS REALLY GROWING...
I CAN SEE THE NEW SIGN IN MY DAD'S SHOP NOW.... "HAIRCUTS-TEN DOLLARS"
SCHULZ

I'VE NEVER BEEN SO MAD IN ALL MY LIFE!
I WENT DOWN TO THE STORE TO GET A HALLOWEEN MASK AND THEY WERE ALL OUT OF THEM!
AREN'T THEY GOING TO ORDER ANY MORE?
HA! ARE YOU KIDDING?
THEY WERE BUSY PUTTING UP CHRISTMAS DECORATIONS!
SCHULZ

Z
Z
Z Z Z Z Z Z Z Z Z Z

LOOK IT'S A PICTURE OF SALLY, CHARLIE BROWN'S NEW BABY SISTER..
H ISN'T SHE UTE?
SHE'S REAL CUTE
THATS SUCH A CUTE PICTURE
SHE SURE IS CUTE, CHARLIE BROWN
SHE'S REAL CUTE
YES SHE'S REAL CUTE
IF THEY EVER TOOK "CUTE" OUT OF THE ENGLISH LANGUAGE, WE'D ALL PERISH!
SCHULZ

YOU THINK YOUR SALLY IS CUTE..YOU SHOULD SEE **HIM**!
HIM? "HIM" WHO?
OH, GOOD GRIEF!
SCHULZ

THAT'S NOT A REAL BABY! THAT'S JUST A DOG DRESSED UP LIKE A BABY!
GOO!
SCHULZ

WHAT WAS THAT?
WHAT WAS WHAT?
I THOUGHT I HEARD SOMETHING OUT BY THE FRONT DOOR..
CHARLIE BROWN HAS HAD TOO MUCH ON HIS MIND LATELY...HE'S CRACKING UP!
ANYONE CARE FOR A FUZZY BABY?
SCHULZ

LOOK, THIS IS YOUR BABY, NOT MINE! I HAVE MY OWN BABY SISTER AT HOME!
YOU WERE THE ONE WHO PUT THE BONNET ON HIM... NOW YOU TAKE CARE OF HIM!
I'M NOT INTERESTED ANY MORE.. I HAVE OTHER THINGS TO DO!
YOU'RE A POOR EXCUSE FOR A MOTHER!!
MAMA!
SCHULZ

HERE, SNOOPY, LET ME TAKE THAT STUPID BONNET OFF YOUR HEAD..
THERE!
BOY, I'M GLAD THAT SILLY BUSINESS IS OVER..
I WASN'T SURE WHETHER I WAS GOING TO END UP IN AN ORPHANAGE OR AT THE HUMANE SOCIETY!
SNOOPY
SCHULZ

I'VE NEVER FELT SO DEPRESSED BEFORE...
WELL, I WISH I KNEW WHAT TO SAY, CHARLIE BROWN, BUT YOU'RE A HARD PERSON TO HELP...
YOU MEAN I HAVE A PERSONALITY SO COMPLICATED THAT IT DEFIES ANALYSIS?
NO, I MEAN YOU HAVE A PERSONALITY SO **SIMPLE** THAT IT DEFIES ANALYSIS!
SCHULZ

HAVING A BABY SISTER HAS MADE A DIFFERENT PERSON OUT OF ME..
YOU JUST THINK IT HAS, CHARLIE BROWN...YOU SEE, YOU'RE A "STATUS SEEKER"..
YOU JUST WANT SOMETHING THAT WILL BUILD YOU UP IN THE EYES OF THE OTHER KIDS IN THE NEIGHBORHOOD..
YOU COULD HAVE ACCOMPLISHED THE SAME THING WITH AN AUTOGRAPHED BASEBALL!
SCHULZ

BOY! WHEN I SIT UP HERE, I CAN SEE FOR MILES!
SNOOPY
I CAN SEE THE ENTIRE CONTINENT!
I CAN SEE THE WHOLE WORLD!
I CAN SEE CLEAR OVER TO THE NEXT YARD!
SCHULZ

DID YOU KNOW THAT CRICKETS CHIRP BY RUBBING PARTS OF THEIR FORE-WINGS TOGETHER?
NO, I'VE ALWAYS THOUGHT THEY USED THEIR HIND LEGS..
A POPULAR MISCONCEPTION!
SCHULZ

ALL RIGHT, SO SHE SHOULDN'T HAVE HUNG IT OUTSIDE WHEN IT WAS SO COLD!

YOU'RE LUCKY MOM EVEN
WASHES YOUR BLANKET!

HOW WAS SHE TO KNOW IT WOULD FREEZE?!

DO YOU REALIZE THAT WE STILL HAVEN'T SEEN SALLY, CHARLIE BROWN?
YES, TELL US WHAT SHE LOOKS LIKE
WELL, SHE'S SORT OF...
NOT THE POSITIVE DETAILS.. THE NEGATIVE DETAILS...
YES, JUST TELL US THAT SHE DOESN'T LOOK LIKE YOU!
SCHULZ

I THINK I KNOW WHAT YOUR TROUBLE IS, CHARLIE BROWN
NOW THAT ALL THE THRILL AND EXCITEMENT OF YOUR BABY SISTER BEING BORN IS OVER, YOU'RE HAVING AN EMOTIONAL LETDOWN
DID YOU HAVE AN EMOTIONAL LETDOWN AFTER LINUS WAS BORN?
I DIDN'T GET A CHANCE. JUST SEEING HIM WAS A LETDOWN!

SO WHAT WOULD BE SO TERRIBLE IF MY OWN BABY SISTER LOOKED LIKE **ME**?
YOU DON'T UNDERSTAND, CHARLIE BROWN
LOOKS AREN'T IMPORTANT TO A BOY...
BUT A GIRL **MUST** HAVE A PRETTY FACE!

LISTEN TO THIS, CHARLIE BROWN...
IT SAYS HERE THAT THERE ARE OVER SIX HUNDRED AND SEVENTY THOUSAND DIFFERENT KINDS OF INSECTS!
WOW!
TAKE COMFORT, LITTLE FELLOW.. YOU ARE NOT ALONE!
SCHULZ

I'M INTERESTED IN LEARNING HOW TO DEVELOP A REAL CONCERN FOR OTHERS..
YOU MEAN YOU WANT TO BE CONCERNED ABOUT THOSE WHO ARE LESS FORTUNATE THAN YOU?
NO, I WANT TO BE CONCERNED ABOUT THOSE WHO ARE MORE FORTUNATE THAN I AM..
I WANT TO BRING THEM DOWN TO MY LEVEL!
SCHULZ

SOMETIMES I LISTEN TO MY BABY SISTER CRYING AT NIGHT, AND IT TEARS MY HEART OUT!
HE WORLD IS ILLED WITH ROUBLE, AND HE'S SO NNOCENT
INNOCENT? SHE'S JUST **HUNGRY**, CHARLIE BROWN!
THAT MAKES ME FEEL EVEN WORSE..
THE WORLD IS IN TURMOIL, AND MY BABY SISTER IS STARVING TO DEATH!
OH, GOOD GRIEF
SCHULZ

EVERY DAY THE PAPERS ARE FULL OF HORRIBLE THINGS!
I HATE TO SEE LITTLE SALLY, GROW UP IN SUCH A WORLD!
DON'T LOOK SO MUCH ON THE DARK SIDE, CHARLIE BROWN... LOOK ON THE BRIGHT SIDE.. THINK OF THE ADVANCEMENTS...
..BY THE TIME SHE GROWS UP, THERE'LL BE THREE MAJOR LEAGUES!

IT'S ALL RIGHT FOR YOU TO BE COMPLACENT, LINUS...
YOU DON'T HAVE A BABY SISTER TO WORRY ABOUT! I TELL YOU THE WORLD IS GETTING WORSE ALL THE TIME!
MURDERS, ROBBERIES, AUTOMOBILE ACCIDENTS, BLACKMAIL, ALL SORTS OF TERRIBLE THINGS!
DON'T FORGET ABOUT KICKING DOGS...PEOPLE ARE ALWAYS KICKING DOGS, TOO..
SCHULZ

I THINK THE WORLD IS MUCH BETTER TODAY THAN IT WAS, SAY, FIVE YEARS AGO..
HOW CAN YOU SAY THAT? DON'T YOU EVER READ THE PAPERS? DON'T YOU EVER LISTEN TO THE RADIO?
HOW CAN YOU STAND THERE, AND TELL ME THIS IS A BETTER WORLD?
I'M IN IT NOW!
SCHULZ

SO YOU THINK THE WORLD IS GETTING BETTER?
WELL, IF YOU'VE GOT SO MUCH CONFIDENCE IN THE WORLD'S GETTING BETTER, HOW COME YOU HANG ON TO THAT BLANKET?
TOUCHÉ!
SCHULZ

WHAT ARE YOU TWO STANDING HERE LOOKING SO WORRIED ABOUT?
WE'RE AFRAID OF THE FUTURE!
ARE YOU WORRIED ABOUT ANYTHING IN PARTICULAR?
OH, NO... WE'RE WORRIED ABOUT EVERYTHING!
YES, OUR WORRYING IS VERY BROADMINDED!
SCHULZ

IT'S FANTASTIC!
I'M PERFECTLY CLEAN NOW, BUT JUST LET ME STEP OUT OF THE HOUSE FOR ONE MINUTE...
WHAM!
YOU KNOW WHAT I AM? I'M A **DUST** MAGNET!
SCHULZ

I ENVY YOU, SNOOPY...YOU DON'T HAVE TO WORRY ABOUT ANYTHING!
YOU DON'T HAVE TO WORRY ABOUT THE FUTURE OF THE WORLD OR ABOUT INFLATION OR ABOUT ANYTHING!!
I WONDER WHERE MY NEXT MEAL IS COMING FROM!

BOY, IT'S TOUGH TO BE A DOG WHEN IT RAINS!
OF COURSE, I'M LUCKIER THAN A LOT OF DOGS.... AT LEAST I HAVE A DOG HOUSE TO GO HOME TO...
SCHULZ

MOM'S GOING DOWNTOWN, LINUS... DO YOU WANT HER TO GET YOU ANYTHING?
TELL HER I NEED A NEW COWBOY HAT...
WHAT SIZE?
MEDIOCRE!
SCHULZ

SNOOPY, HAVE YOU EVER FELT THAT YOU WERE A BORE?
HAVE YOU EVER FELT THAT PEOPLE WERE BORED BY EVERYTHING YOU SAID?
VE YOU EVER FELT THAT THEY RENT'T THE LEAST BIT TERESTED IN ANYTHING YOU..
Z

CATCH THE SNOWFLAKES ON YOUR TONGUE, LUCY!
IT'S TOO EARLY... I NEVER EAT JANUARY SNOWFLAKES... I ALWAYS WAIT UNTIL FEBRUARY...
THEY SURE LOOK RIPE TO ME!

I'M THE KIND OF PERSON WHO IS KIND OF HARD TO GET TO KNOW, I GUESS..
MY PERSONALITY DOESN'T LIE RIGHT ON THE SURFACE...THE REAL ME IS DEEP...BUT I'M WELL WORTH ALL THE TIME IT TAKES TO UNDERSTAND ME...
IN OTHER WORDS, TO KNOW ME, IS TO LOVE ME!
* SIGH *

I GUESS I LET TOO MANY THINGS BOTHER ME...
I SEEM TO GET UPSET BY ANY LITTLE THING I HEAR
I THINK I'M GOING TO HAVE TO ERECT SORT OF A MENTAL FENCE TO KEEP UNPLEASANT NEWS OUT OF MY MIND...
DON'T MAKE IT A PICKET FENCE...THEY'RE AWFULLY HARD TO PAINT!
SCHULZ

MY GRAMMA IS STAYING WITH US FOR A FEW DAYS...
LAST NIGHT WE ALL WENT TO THE SHOW EXCEPT GRAMMA.. SHE DOESN'T LIKE SHOWS...
SO SHE STAYED HOME ALONE THEN, HUH?
NO, WE GOT A GRAMMA-SITTER!
SCHULZ

HERE'S THE FAITHFUL DOG FOLLOWING THE KIDS TO SCHOOL..
HERE'S THE FAITHFUL DOG SITTING DOWN OUTSIDE WHILE ALL THE KIDS GO INSIDE..
HERE'S THE FAITHFUL DOG LYING DOWN OUTSIDE WAITING FOR SCHOOL TO LET OUT...
HERE'S THE FAITHFUL DOG SUDDENLY REALIZING HE'S WASTING HIS TIME!
SCHULZ

I HEAR YOU KIND OF LIKE YOUR NEW TEACHER, LINUS...
CHARLIE BROWN, I HAVE THE GREATEST TEACHER IN THE WHOLE WORLD! SHE'S A GEM AMONG GEMS!
SIGH
I NEVER REALIZED THAT THE NATIONAL EDUCATION ASSOCIATION TURNED OUT SUCH A FINE PRODUCT!
SCHULZ

WHAT'S THIS ABOUT YOU AND A "MISS OTHMAR"? WHO IN THE WORLD IS MISS OTHMAR?
SHE'S MY TEACHER...SHE UNDERSTANDS ME!
EITHER SHE'S A GENIUS, OR SHE'S NEW ON THE JOB
SCHULZ